'It's Roy Plomley—when you've got rid of everybody
and you're completely alone, which eight records . . .'

'Sorry, luv, that's an old trick—you keep me talking
while your husband fills up the swimming pool.'

MAC'S
Daily Mail
CARTOONS

PENTAGON

© Daily Mail 1975
Printed in Great Britain for
David Foster Ltd, 20 Kewferry Drive
Northwood, Middx.
by Redwood Burn Limited
Trowbridge & Esher
SBN: 0 904288 05 6

'I think it's another canvasser, Arthur—
he's promising the Kingdom of Heaven . . .'

'It's only more Oxfam leaflets with pathetic pictures of freezing, starving Britons.'

'Remember the old days, when they were forever trying to sneak in?'

'Do you think this really IS extra security? Or is it Denis
Healey making sure we don't escape before Tuesday?'

'O'Flaherty should crawl through any second now
—he's been on hunger strike for three months'

'C'mon, old boy—they've leaked the name of Mr 'Y'—don't you want to know who it is?'

'Will ye be long splittin' that atom, Seamus?
They've found the "bomb factory" next door'

'Honestly, I just didn't think that compulsory disclosure of MPs'
interests, open to the public, would be quite like this, Angela.'

'Dear Mr Foot . . . we have got Barbara Castle,
and unless you agree to our demands . . .'

'She's been like this ever since they discovered
that £500,000 worth of porn in her cowshed.'

'It was my fault really—you know how wild
he gets if I forget to pack his bananas'

'It was unfortunate the technicians blacking me out half way through
your operation, Mr Spinks, but at least you won't have to worry about
paying for family planning from now on.'

'Sex, sex, sex!—That's all you ever think about.'

'A letter from the bank saying we're £500 overdrawn?
—Obviously another of those damned forgeries, darling.'

'Good heavens, is it that time already ?—We've
missed the Chancellor's speech!'

'Dear Mammy, if you could manage just one more
cake—this time with a sparking plug in it . . .'

'Surprise, surprise, Mum and Dad—to cheer you up after your wet
Bank Holiday, we've recorded the entire Reading Pop Festival. . . .'

'It's all fairly straightforward—if you get any trouble, you just plug
into the right number and BOOM! his identity card device explodes . . !'

'Hell, don't worry, son—anyone can make a mistake'

'All the controversy over who'll move in here is over, Effendi—we just bought the place.'

'Take no notice, Mary—he's *still* pestering
for a coalition'

'Let's see now—if Heath resigns, there's Whitelaw, Du Cann, Thatcher, Joseph—who else could rescue the party?'

'. . . with one bound Noddy was by her side, his little bell tinkling . . .'

'. . . and my total earnings for 1973–74 were . . . oh, dear, I
seem to have someone's tax forms mixed up with my speech.'

'Miss Ibbotsen has made the tea, sir—could you
open the safe so we can get the sugar out?'

'Now, Mr Amin—before your little Idi was born, can
you remember how tight your underpants were?'

'You go ahead, miss—we'll see you don't
have any more trouble from Peeping Toms.'

'Oh, my God—she's letting father out!'

'It's Idi Amin! He must've heard about our defence cuts.'

'Me too—I'm going to Britain for the January sales. There's lots of bargains—Aston Martin's firm, Burmah Oil, Leyland. . . .'

'I'll repeat that, Lord—Wedgie Benn's address is . . .'

'Some of the lads got so sick about the Tunnel being
cancelled, they decided to emigrate to Australia'

'Good Lord! I had no idea you did a paper round, Hetherington.'

'I wonder how long her "Hello big boy, my you're looking scrumptious!" greetings will last, once she's elected?'

'Your wife is going to be busier than ever now, Thatcher
—shouldn't you be thinking of getting a housekeeper?'

One small step for woman—a giant leap for womankind.

'Good heavens! They've renamed it—
Rodin's "Battle for the Tory leadership".'

'Course I've got a lot of admirers—on my
money I'm a very attractive proposition'

'That's right, sir—we've got the railway militants in the pipeline'

'It's the result of a little referendum we had—"Do you
think signalmen should stay members of the community?"'

'When I voted for radio, nobody said anything about
fighting the flab with Terry Wogan every day!'

'That's the third round he's insisted on buying—I hope he doesn't consider that's Britain's contribution to the E.E.C.'

'Good heaven's yes, Modom—with petrol the price it is, our
do-it-yourself, inflatable plastic oil rigs are selling like hot cakes.'

'It's a smashing set of soldiers, Dad—tiny little dustbins,
an employment exchange, miniature redundancy money . . .'

'Mum—how would you fancy entering for
the glamorous granny competition next year?'

'Trust me, Camrade—it's the
safest way to travel at the moment.'

'There'll be hell to pay if anyone finds out about the whisky and wild, wild women . . .'

'Do you think I could collect your union
dues now, lads? I'm a bit short of petrol.'

'... thought it prudent to stock up on a little gin—
incidentally, if you want tonic, its in the bath upstairs ...'

'. . . and finally, Mauritius has rejected John Stone-
house's request for asylum, but accepted mine. . . .'

'If everyone in the country worked as hard as
he does—we'd soon be back on our feet again.'

'I said I'll just exercise the dog
—spelt E - X - E - R - C - I - S - E'

'Daddy won't give in to the stable lads—he's been
up since 6.30 this morning mucking out the stables'

'Mr Benn—I trust you have consulted your wife
about your takeover plans for Miss Onassis?'

'No thanks, mate—can't read'

'I'm going back to work, lads! If they can do
this at Fords, what might our lot do to us?'

'Ol' brown eyes is back and wants to know
what you've done with his colour telly'

'Dear moderate . . . There will be a tedious, boring old branch meeting to vote in a union official on Wednesday night. But it will probably be a cold night and there's a good programme on telly, so if you'll take my advice. . . .'

'Congratulations on being fully qualified—now then, I believe they
have a few vacancies for counter assistants at Woolworth's . . .'